mad about
Maths

shape
and
space

Adrian & Jeni Pinel

ReD
KiTE

Welcome to Mad About Maths: Shape & Space!

Magical mazes, mysterious mirror trickery, paper folding and picture puzzles – shapes and spaces have never been so much fun to discover. From the patterns on your wallpaper to the square of your computer screen, they're everywhere – and they're all mathematical!

Each double page in this book has a different mathematical theme on it for you to get to grips with. Follow the instructions on how to make models or solve puzzles, and keep an eye out for 'info' boxes, handy hints and clues which will give you a little bit of extra help along the way.

At the back of this book, you'll find a 6-page section full of different things for you to use throughout the book – coloured or patterned shape pieces, isometric paper, templates to make and 3-D shape 'modules'. For example, take a look at Terrific Tangrams on pages 6–7. You'll notice that you need to use tangram pieces to complete these puzzles yourself – so just turn to the section at the back and press out the ready-made tangram pieces you will find there.

You may want to use some of these shapes at bigger sizes or use them again and again. Simply press them out and photocopy them as many times as you want. You can give some to your friends to have a go with, too!

Above all, have fun with this book!

Contents

shape and space

Amazing Mazes

People have been making mazes for hundreds of years – in gardens, inside buildings, on hillsides – even underground! Here are some simple magic mazes made up of a number of 'rooms', with an entrance and an exit.

Elephant maze

A hungry elephant who loves cakes is about to enter the maze. She will only go into a room if she can see a cake in it. When she leaves a room it is always empty! Follow her through the maze and out again to see how many cakes she eats.

Now try this!

More cakes magically appear in each room when the elephant leaves the maze. If she goes in again at the entrance, can she find a different path through the maze?

How many routes can you find and how many cakes get eaten for each route? Now, you should be able to work out which path will give the elephant the most cakes to eat.

Pirate treasure

This pirate is trying to collect up the bags of gold that he has stolen on the high seas. See how many different routes he can take through the maze and work out which route will give him the most treasure. Remember that he only enters a room if there is gold in it and he never leaves any behind when he passes through a room.

Make up your own room mazes and think of stories to go with them. Now challenge your friends to solve them.

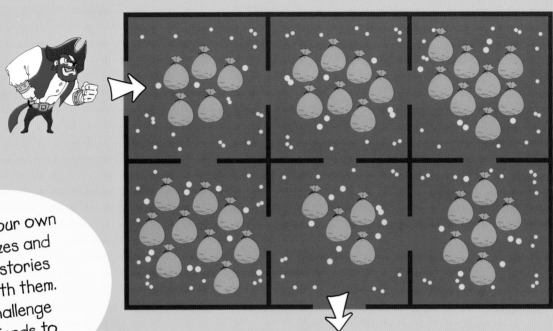

Collecting carrots

This rabbit wants to take some carrots home for tea. He has lots of brothers and sisters to share them with so he will need plenty. Count how many he can collect.

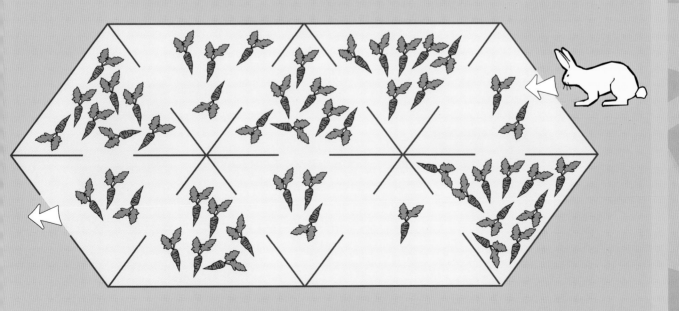

Terrific Tangrams

A tangram is a shape that is divided into different pieces, which can then be rearranged to make lots of shapes. The first tangram had seven pieces. It was invented in China a very long time ago – so has been explored by people in many cultures for more than a millennium!

Two-piece tangram taster

This is a simple two-piece square tangram which you can cut into two pieces to make new shapes. Use the template provided to transfer the tangram on to thin card and then see what shapes and pictures you can create.

Now you've got the hang of them, here are two of the shapes that you can make with the two-piece tangram, but you must follow this rule. RULE: Whole sides must match whole sides with corners meeting each other.

How many different shapes can be made using this rule? Watch out for shapes that are flipped or turned – these may look different but they are still the same shape.

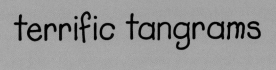

Tangram tessellations

Take some copies of your new shapes by photocopying or drawing around them onto coloured paper. Fit them together to begin a tessellation like this one.

Why not try tessellating just one of your tangram shapes. See what different patterns you can make.

Now try your hand at making these tangrams: a three-piece tangram and the original Chinese tangram with seven pieces. Use the templates provided to create them and see what amazing shapes you can make from the pieces.

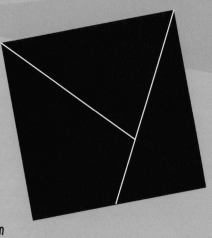

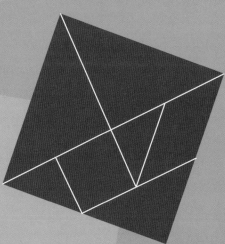

Picture puzzles

The Chinese often made picture puzzles using tangram pieces. Here are three outlines that can be made from one or other of these two tangrams. Can you see where the pieces will fit?

Devious Dissections

Dissection puzzles are great fun and will have you scratching your head for hours. Use the templates provided to make your own shapes for these puzzles which can then be divided up to make all sorts of different shapes.

Handy hint

Try out your ideas by making some paper squares using the templates. There are two easy ways of making the larger square. One way has four pieces fitting together, and the other needs five pieces to make the square.

Clever cuts

Here is a dissection puzzle using two identical squares. First of all, cut out two squares of the same size using the templates provided.

Now, look at the squares and see if you can work out how to cut up one or both of the squares so that the smaller pieces of square form another larger square when put together.

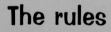

The rules

RULE 1: The larger square must be a solid shape. It should not have any holes inside it or any over-lapping pieces.

RULE 2: You can only cut in a straight line.

Tricky triangles

Make two identical equilateral triangles using the template provided. Now try to turn them into a regular hexagon! You will use just four pieces to make the new shape. It's easier than you think!

INFO!
Remember that an equilateral triangle is a triangle where all three sides are the same length.

Now make three small equilateral triangles into one larger equilateral triangle. You should cut each small triangle into two pieces.

Snip snip!

Look at this cross made up of five identical squares. Can you turn it into one larger square? Try making the cross and then turning it around until you see a 'nearly square'. The answer uses five pieces.

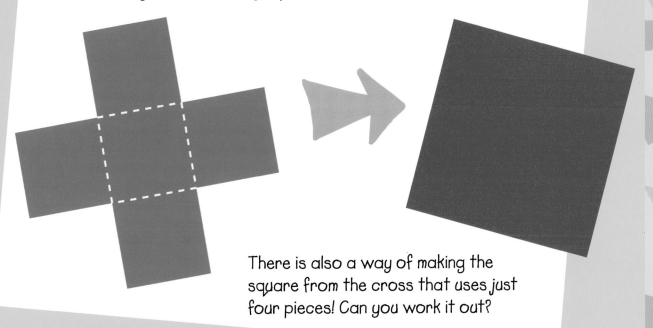

There is also a way of making the square from the cross that uses just four pieces! Can you work it out?

Puzzling Pieces

You've seen how shapes can be cut up and rearranged to make others, here are some shapes that can be cut up into two or more shapes that are exactly the same. You wouldn't guess by looking at them!

Congruent shapes

These two shapes are exactly the same so they are called congruent shapes.

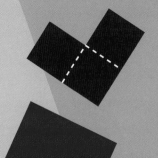

If you fit them together, they make a new shape, but it's not always easy to decide where one shape begins and another ends.
Hide the join and you have a puzzle!
Shapes like these can have two, three or more congruent pieces hidden within them.

Handy hint
Try turning the shapes around and looking at them from a different angle. Look for similar shapes within the outline.

Find the join
Take a look at these three outlines. They are called congruent halves because two identical shapes are hidden within them. Can you find where the two shapes meet?

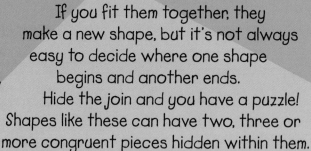

Triple trouble

To solve these puzzle shapes, can you work out how three identical shapes fit together to make each outline?

When you have found the congruent shape that makes these outlines, make a puzzle for your friends by using the shapes four or five times to make new outlines.

andy hint

You may find it easier to make copies of the shapes before trying the puzzles on these two pages.

Creating congruent shapes

Arrangements of five squares are called 'pentominoes'. They make good shapes for creating puzzles like these (and some of them are made up of two congruent shapes already).

Put two or more pentominoes together to make puzzles for your friends to solve.

shape and space

Clever Circuits

These squares and hexagons have curved and straight tracks on them. They can be put together to make patterns that are called circuits.

You'll need at least six of each tile to solve these puzzles. Use the templates provided – you can photocopy them and cut them out or trace the designs on to clean paper.

Grid action

Try fitting four squares into this grid. How many different ways can you do it? Do the tracks continue from square to square for each one?

Try the same with six hexagon tiles on this hexagonal grid. You could use all of the patterns or try several of the same design to make different circuits.

Puzzling patterns

Now use your tiles to puzzle out how to make these two circuits.

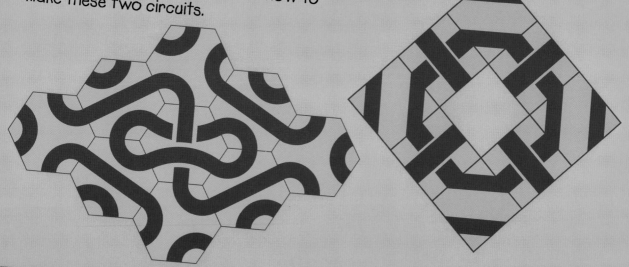

Hexagon challenges

Use your imagination and make up some circuits of your own.

▲ What is the simplest circuit that you can make with the hexagons? You don't have to use every pattern.

▲ Now, make some other circuits that use exactly five hexagon tiles.

▲ How many different circuits can you make using six hexagon tiles?

▲ Can you make a circuit where the track crosses over itself?

▲ Try making circuits with seven to twelve tiles. Challenge a friend to make some circuits too.

Busy Borders

All over the world, people make patterns – on pottery, in weaving clothes, around their homes. The ones around the edges of pots, along hems of clothes, or along the edge of a wall are border patterns. You can make border patterns using the squares and hexagons that you used to make circuits. Look at the examples on these pages.

Linking squares

Use the squares from the previous pages to make these two border patterns. You will need three rows of tiles, placed with their corners pointing up and down.

Can you see that each pattern repeats itself and is symmetrical in some way.

Linking hexagons

With the hexagon patterns, again with corners pointing up and down (rather than flat sides), you can make a pattern with either two or three rows.

Can you make these two patterns with your tiles? And then continue them on. Now design some border patterns of your own.

Cunning codes

How can you keep a record of the patterns you particularly like? Drawing them is one way, but it would be much easier if you could use a code for each pattern, just like spies! For example, the first two patterns of squares could be written down as:

We use a different letter for each patterned tile and the number next to it will tell us which way up the square should be placed. The pattern on each square tile has two lines of symmetry so there are only two different ways of laying these tiles.

Can you work out the two patterns and discover which tile is A and B? And, can you see the difference between B1 and B2?

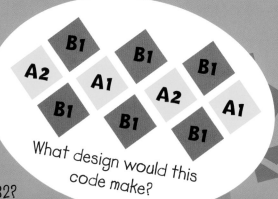

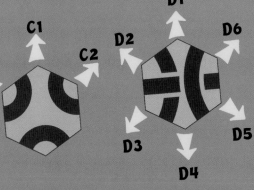

What design would this code make?

Placing the hexagons

The problem with coding the hexagons is that there are many ways of placing them!

To start with, lets call them hexagons C, D, E, F and G. If you look carefully at the designs, you will notice that the most simple tiles are C and E because they are the most symmetrical.

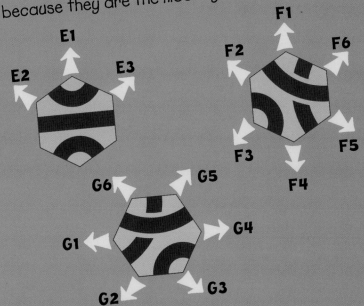

Tile C has only two different ways of being placed – C1 and C2. E has three different ways of being placed – E1, E2 and E3. The other three hexagons have six different ways of being placed.

Look at these coded hexagons, Can you work out the codes for the two hexagon border patterns opposite?

Wonderful Walls

Some patterns are spread all over a surface – think of a paved area, a piece of cloth or a wall. It's quite easy to extend a border pattern to cover a much larger area. Here are some examples to start you off. See if you can make these patterns from the codes.

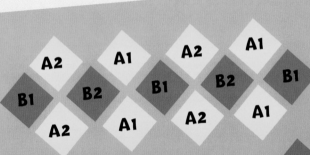

Building walls

Here is the code for a border pattern using the square tiles. How would you continue it above and below these rows?

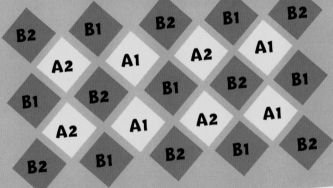

If you continue it by repeating the rows, what shapes begin to appear? Its code would build out as shown here.

Work with a friend to find other ways of continuing the pattern.

Here's a much more interesting pattern. Try making it yourself. Can you code it with A1, A2, B1 and B2 ?

Try planning and making a piece of wall pattern as big as this with the squares. (You might need to make some more first.) Record it with a code and then ask a friend to try and make it from your code.

Easy walls

With the hexagons – if you are going to keep a record of your codes – it is easier to start with combinations

of tiles C and E because they are the most symmetrical. Try making these patterns and then work out their codes.

The first hexagon pattern above is a border pattern with this code. Can you make it?

| C2 | E2 | C2 | E2 | C2 |
| E2 | C2 | E2 | C2 | E2 |

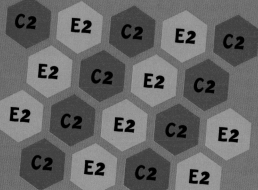

It can be extended to this pattern. Make it and then try swapping C1s for all the C2s and compare the patterns.

The second hexagon border can be extended to this pattern.

Try other possibilities and keep a coded record of your favourite.

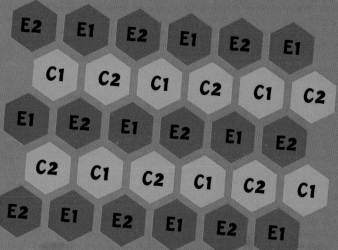

Mirror Magic

Mirrors are fascinating to experiment with. Try looking around corners with a mirror or reflecting light onto objects with one. For these puzzles you will need two plastic mirrors, hinged as shown below with masking tape so that you can change the angle between the mirrors.

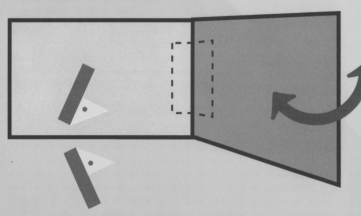

Make the picture

To solve the two puzzles on these pages, you must place the hinged mirrors on the main picture (the one in the square) so that the reflections form a new picture. One of the pictures in each puzzle is not possible – which one?

Count the dots

Before you use the mirrors, try to imagine where you might place them to make the three pictures below. Where would you position the mirror join? At what angle will the mirrors need to be? Can you find the picture which can't be made with the mirrors?

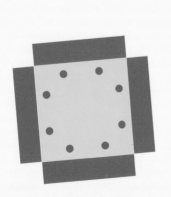
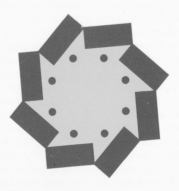

Stars and squares

Here's another puzzle for you to try. Position the mirrors on the main picture and see if you can make the three pictures below. Now can you find the odd one out?

Try this on a friend – don't forget to tell them that one picture can't be made!

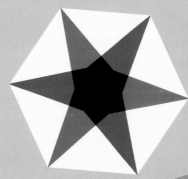

Handy hint

Look at the colours on the shape that you are trying to make as a clue for how it could be done.

You could even try to divide up the new picture into similar shapes to find out which parts of the original shape should be reflected.

Making mirror puzzles

Mirror puzzles are great to try out on your friends and family, and fun to make as well. The easiest way of making some similar puzzles of your own for others to solve is to use a sheet of squared paper or square dot paper. Draw a simple picture or shape on it and then use your hinged mirrors to make some new pictures appear. Copy three or more of these on to some clean paper.

You now have a mirror puzzle to try out on your friends. You could also draw another picture that can almost, but not quite, be made!

Module Mayhem

Just as you can play with plastic bricks and blocks to build all sorts of shapes and forms, using only paper you can make 'modules' which slot together to make 3-D shapes. See if you can make these modules and then fit them together for some 3-D magic!

The square-based module

- Use the template provided to make a square from coloured paper. Fold it in half. Then unfold it to show the crease.

- Fold each half in half again, bringing the outside edges in to the centre. Press the folds down firmly.

- Fold up the bottom left corner to the opposite side, again pressing firmly.

- Turn the whole thing upside-down and fold up the bottom left corner the same way.

- Now tuck away the two large triangles by opening out the shape and pushing the triangular flaps under the rectangular folds. Your paper should now look like this.

- Fold back and tuck away the two small triangles at the top and bottom. You now have a parallelogram.

- Turn the parallelogram over to the plain side and fold in the two end triangles firmly to make a square.

- Fold the square in half along the joining line to make a triangle and press down really firmly. You have your first square-based module! Now you can use the two flapping triangles – like wings – to slot into other modules to make a strong edge.

The triangle-based module

▲ Use the template at the back of this book to make an equilateral triangle from coloured paper. Fold your triangle symmetrically in half through all three corners, unfolding it each time so that the creases show.

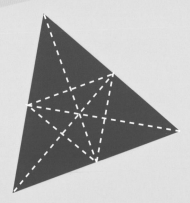

▲ Next, fold and unfold each corner in turn down to the middle of its opposite side, so that you have three more creases.

▲ Cut along the crease lines from each corner as far as the sides of the central upside-down triangle. You now have two small triangles at each corner.

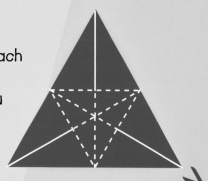

▲ Working your way round the triangle, fold in each left-hand small triangle towards the centre, tucking them into each other. You have your first triangle-based module!

Shaping up

Make lots of each shape with bright and colourful paper: you need four triangle modules to make a triangular pyramid – a regular tetrahedron – and six square modules to make a cube. By fitting together two 'wings' on every edge, experiment with the modules to make different shapes and structures.

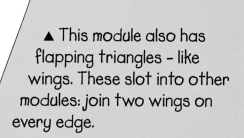

▲ This module also has flapping triangles – like wings. These slot into other modules: join two wings on every edge.

shape and space

A New Dimension

No, it's not spots in front of your eyes – this is what a piece of isometric paper looks like! This paper lets us draw 3-D shapes, with their correct lengths, even though they are on 2-D paper!

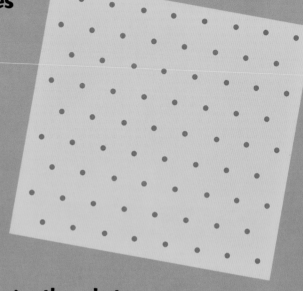

Join the dots

You can join the dots to draw a cube on this paper (it also looks like a regular hexagon split into three diamond shapes). Practise drawing cubes yourself on the paper provided.

Making cubes

Making a 3-D cube from card or paper is really easy. Following the enclosed template, draw and cut out some cubes with 2cm sides. You can stick them together with non-toxic PVA glue or sticky tape and then you're ready to make some really puzzling 3-D shapes.

In mathematics, this 2-D template for a 3-D object is called a 'net'.

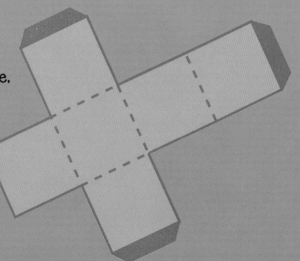

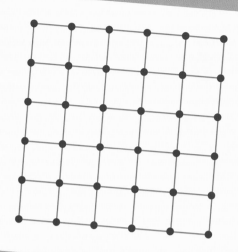

For the following puzzles, you will need at least ten cubes with 2cm-long sides, and the '5 x 5' grid of 2cm squares that is provided (like this one but larger).

If you want to use cubes of a different size, you'll need a bigger or smaller grid depending on the size of the cubes. Why not draw up your own with a ruler and pencil.

Isometric magic

Take these two 4-cube shapes and put them together to make some 8-cube shapes, then draw them on isometric paper.

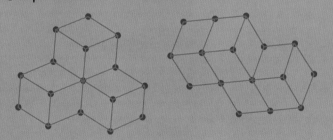

Cube concoctions

Now try making these isometric drawings into 3-D shapes using your cubes and the 5 x 5 grid. How many cubes are these shapes made up of?

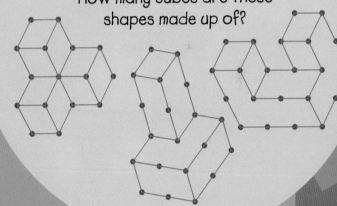

The 3rd dimension

These are isometric drawings of 3-D shapes made from four cubes. Try making them on the 5 x 5 grid (using glue to stick your cubes together, if necessary).

What other arrangements of four cubes can you make? Experiment on the 5 x 5 grid and try drawing them on isometric paper as well. Get your friends to make 3-D shapes from your drawings.

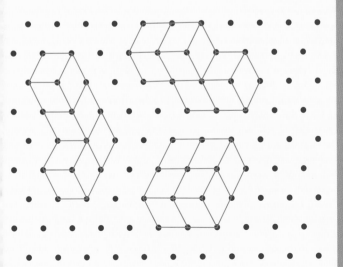

Shady Silhouettes

Silhouettes are the 2-D outlines that you see when you look at any 3-D object face on. Named after Etienne de Silhouette, the Frenchman who developed shadow portraits, silhouettes are a fascinating way of looking at 3-D items. Some shapes are obvious just by looking at their silhouette, but others are much more difficult to 'see'.

What is it?

Shapes made from groups of cubes can have three different silhouettes. These three silhouettes are of the same 3-D shape made from just five identical cubes. Try to work out how the cubes are placed (you can use the cubes you made for pages 22-23).

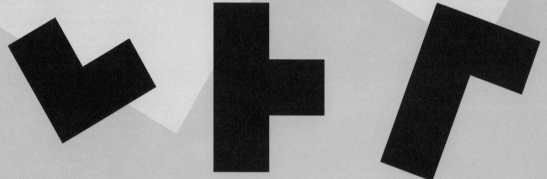

Silhouette shapes

Here are three silhouette puzzles using different numbers of cubes. Before you try them, make some arrangements of four or five cubes yourself and draw their silhouette shapes on to 2cm-squared paper. Get your friends to make some too. Swap them with each other and work out ways to solve them.

This 3-D shape is made with seven cubes. Can you see it?

This 3-D shape is made from eight cubes. How are they arranged?

How many cubes are needed to make these two 3-D shapes?

Special silhouettes

Some 3-D shapes made from cubes have the same silhouette from all three directions. A single cube is the simplest example of this. Think of some other shapes that do this as well.

Here is the silhouette of one of these special shapes. Can you work out how many cubes you would need to make it? You may be surprised just how few it actually takes!

Playful Pop-ups

You can make pop-ups to surprise your family and friends from simple 3-D shapes. Using cereal boxes or similar card, shapes fold flat and you can use elastic bands and staples to make them pop up!

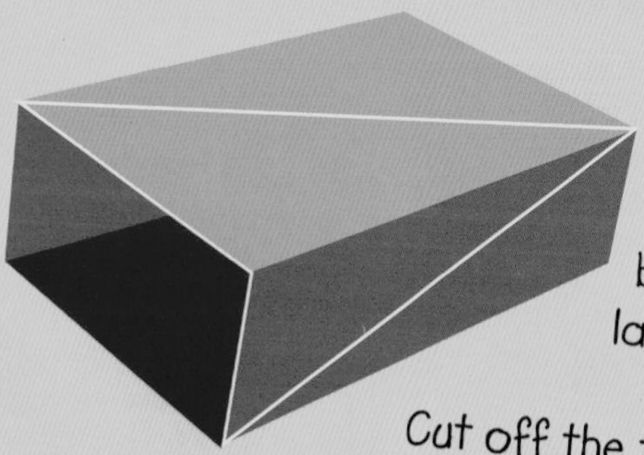

Pop-up by hand

For the first shape you will need an empty cereal box, some scissors, a long ruler, a ballpoint pen that no longer works and a large elastic band.

Cut off the top and bottom flaps of the box. Use the ruler and pen to mark all four diagonals of the box with a joined-up zig-zag pattern, as shown here. Press down quite hard with the pen to make a good crease in the cardboard.

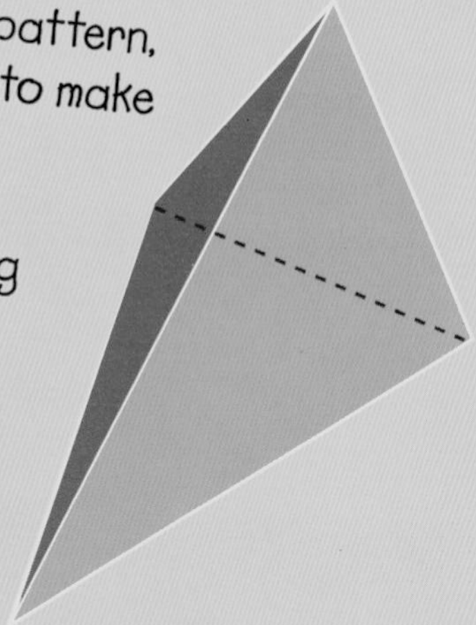

Fold along the creases that you have made, flattening the original edges of the box. Your should find four triangles appearing – instead of four oblongs – as your shape becomes a 3-D skew tetrahedron – a crooked four-sided shape. Wrap the elastic band around the tetrahedron in such a way that it keeps its shape.

Baffling boxes

Use other box shapes or trim cereal boxes to different sizes to make a collection of different tetrahedra.
Are any of your tetrahedra symmetrical? Experiment to work out what box shape you would need to make a symmetrical tetrahedron. Now try joining together several of your tetrahedra to make new shapes.

Pop-ups - no hands!

Use the net below to make a regular octahedron – an eight-sided 3-D shape – from equilateral triangles. You can trace or photocopy the net on to some card and then cut it out, folding it along the dotted lines without flattening the shape.

Assemble the octahedron and stick down the flaps. If you flatten the shape, you should have a 'mouth' on one side. By wrapping an elastic band around the two outer edges of the mouth and securing them to each point with staples, the octahedron will remain flat when pressure is applied and pop up when it is released. Press the octahedron flat between two sheets of card and place it in an envelope. When the card is pulled out of the envelope, the octahedron should pop up into the air!

Handy hint
Try different sizes of elastic bands to make the pop-up work. A good experiment is to hold the octahedron shape upright and place the unstretched elastic band against the closed mouth. Mark where it lies. Staple the elastic band into this position.

Pop-up spectacular

You can also make a pop-up dodecahedron - a twelve-sided 3-D shape. Draw this template of regular pentagons twice on card and cut them out. Fold the outer pentagons inwards (but don't flatten them). Bring the two together and carefully wrap a long elastic band around the points of the hexagons (on the black line) so that they hold together, forming a dodecahedron.

Gently press down on the top central pentagon and the 3-D shape will flatten so that it can be placed under a magazine or book. When someone picks up the magazine, the dodecahedron should pop up and surprise them!

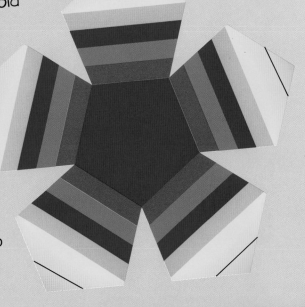

Nearly Nets

It's great fun assembling 3-D shapes from a 2-D template or net (and you've had plenty of practice now). Look at the nets on these two pages and try to work out what shapes they would make. Some of them aren't quite complete – can you finish the net?

INFO!
A polyhedron is a 3-D shape with many flat sides.
A polygon is a figure with many sides or angles.

Perfect net

An easy one for you to start with, this is the net of a square-based pyramid. Trace the shape or draw it using equilateral triangles, fold along the creases and fix it in place with sticky tape.

Handy hint
Try imagining the 'nearly net' folding up to make a box without its lid. Where would you put the lid?

Nifty nets

Most nets of polyhedra (such as a tetrahedron and an octahedron) are almost symmetrical – here are five squares symmetrically arranged that nearly make a cube net. To complete the net you have to decide where the final square could go! There are several different places that would work.

Try some other arrangements of five squares. Which would fold up to make a lidless cube? Where could the final square go in each case?

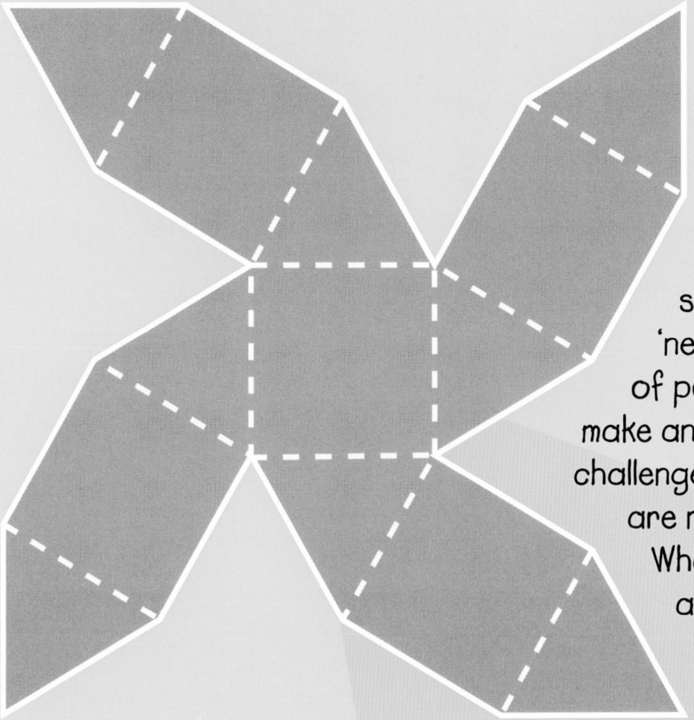

Polyhedra puzzles

When you are given a net all you
have to do to make the 3-D shape
is cut it out, fold along the lines and
stick it together. Here are some
'nearly nets' – symmetrical arrangements
of polygons. Imagine folding them up to
make an incomplete polyhedron. Your
challenge is to decide what extra polygons
are needed and where to place them!
When you think that you know the
answer, trace the nets and make up
the polyhedra. Were you right?

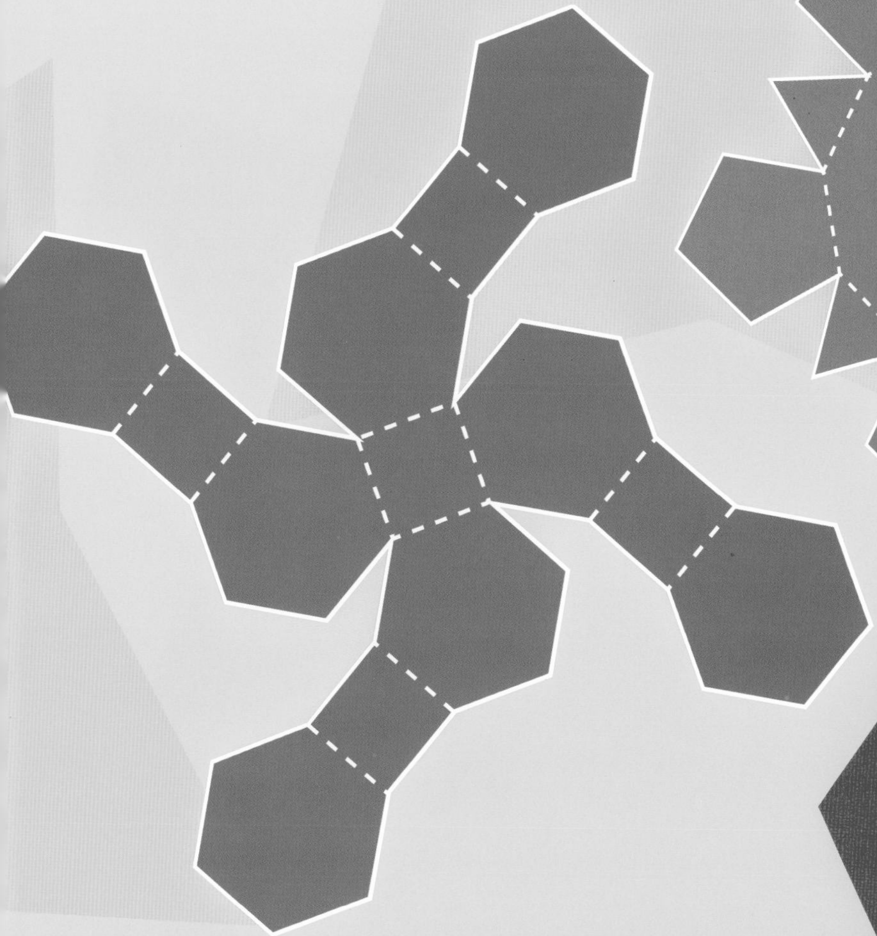

Make up some
symmetrical
arrangements of
polygons that are
nearly nets. Try these
out on your friends.
Can they find the
missing shapes?

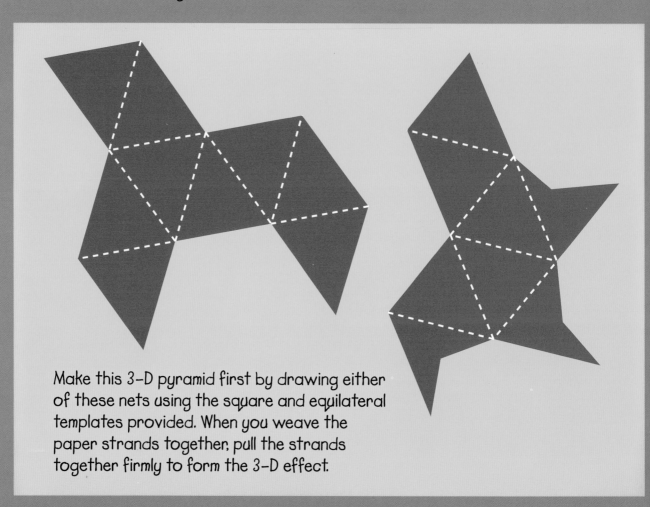

Wacky Weaving

Did you know that you can weave paper just like you can weave thread or plait your hair? By using the nets on these two pages, you can make some fantastic 3-D shapes which fit together without needing glue or sticky tape.

Get weaving

Draw up the nets on these two pages (using the square and equilateral triangle templates provided) so that the sides of each triangle and square are at least 5cm long. Cut out the shapes and also make any necessary cuts along the solid lines marked. Fold along the dotted lines and then 'weave' or 'plait' the paper lengths together, passing each length of paper over and under the other lengths.

Make this 3-D pyramid first by drawing either of these nets using the square and equilateral templates provided. When you weave the paper strands together, pull the strands together firmly to form the 3-D effect.

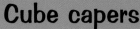

Cube capers

Now try weaving this cube shape. Remember to cut down the solid line. Start by weaving or plaiting the left-hand strand over the centre strand. Then fold the right-hand length back over the top and keep weaving!

Where do the dots go?
This is a fun way of making dice for games with your friends. It will be easier to draw the dots on before you weave the shape, but can you figure out where they should go?

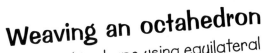

Weaving an octahedron

Draw up this shape using equilateral triangles with 5cm-long sides. This shape is slightly more difficult to make but just keep weaving the two lengths over and under each other, starting with the left strand over the right. The shape should appear by magic.

Why not make your own designs and decorations for the triangles and squares that will show on the outside of the completed shapes?

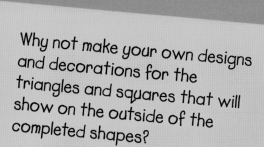

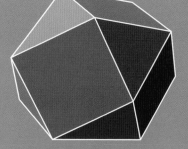

Wild weaving

When you've made these, you could design weaving patterns for some other polyhedra. Try making these two shapes.

Answers

pages 4–5 Amazing Mazes

Elephant maze
There are 4 different routes through the elephant maze.
The most cakes that the elephant can collect is 18.

Pirate treasure
There are 3 different paths through the maze.
The most bags of gold that the pirate can collect is 30 bags.

pages 6–7 Terrific Tangrams

Two-piece tangram taster
There are 8 different ways of arranging the 2-piece tangram (including the square).

Picture puzzles

pages 8–9 Devious Dissections

Clever cuts
Here are two ways of cutting up the small squares to make a large square:

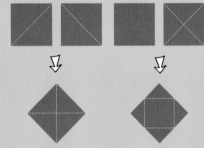

Tricky triangles
Cut up the triangles as shown below to solve these triangle puzzles.

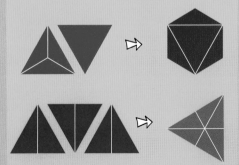

Snip snip!
This is the five-piece solution to this puzzle.

This is how to make the square from just four pieces.

pages 10–11 Puzzling Pieces

Find the join
You can divide up the three shapes as follows:

Triple trouble
This is how the three congruent shapes fit together:

pages 12–13 Clever Circuits

Hexagon challenges
The simplest circuit that you can make with the hexagons:

A circuit which crosses over itself:

pages 18–19 Mirror Magic

Make the picture
The second picture cannot be made with the mirrors.

Stars and square
The second picture cannot be made with the mirrors.

pages 22–23 A New Dimension

Cube concoctions
The first shape is made up of 4 cubes, the second of 6 cubes and the third shape is made up of 6 cubes.

pages 24–25 Shady Silhouettes

What is it?

Silhouette shapes
This is the seven-cube shape: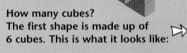

This is the eight-cube shape: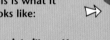

How many cubes?
The first shape is made up of 6 cubes. This is what it looks like:

The second shape is made up of 11 cubes. This is what it looks like:

Special silhouettes
This special silhouette shape can be made up of just 12 cubes. This is what it looks like:

pages 28–29 Nearly Nets

Polyhedra puzzles
Top puzzle: a square is missing.
Centre puzzle: a pentagon and 5 equilateral triangles are missing.
Bottom puzzle: a square is missing.

pages 14–15 Busy Borders

Cunning codes
The code would make this design:

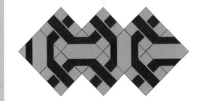

Placing the hexagons
The two hexagon border patterns are:

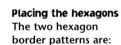

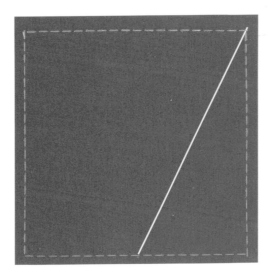

**Two-piece tangram
(page 6)**

Three-piece tangram (page 7)

Chinese tangram (page 7)

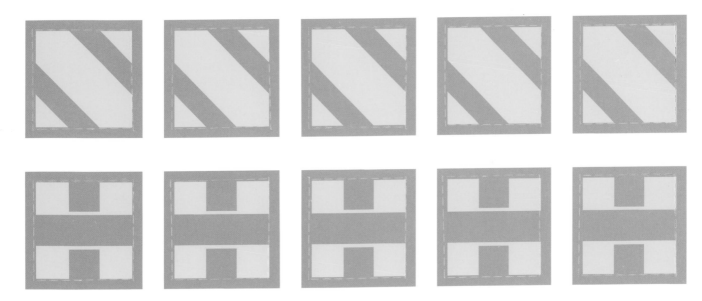

Circuit pieces (pages 12-17)

Squares and
equilateral triangles
(pages 8–9 and 26–31)

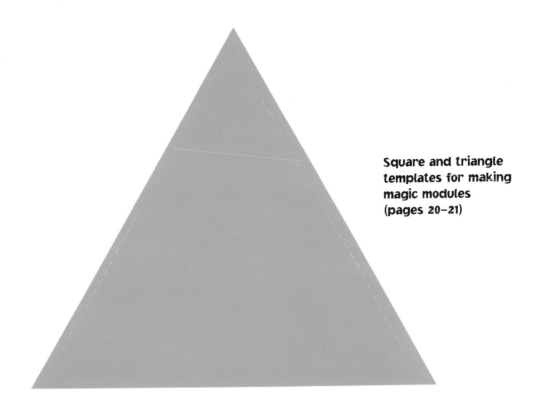

Square and triangle
templates for making
magic modules
(pages 20–21)

Isometric paper (pages 22–23).
Photocopy this page to draw
3-D shapes.

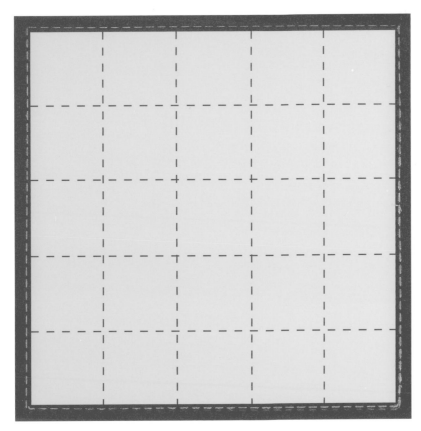

A '5 x 5' grid of 2cm
squares (pages 22–23)

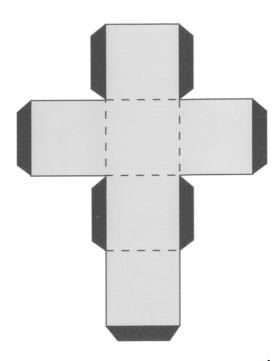

Template for making a cube
to be used with the grid
above (pages 22–23)